CHIRAPTOPHOBIA

A one-act drama by
Hannah Estelle Sears

www.youthplays.com
info@youthplays.com
424-703-5315

COPYRIGHT RULES TO REMEMBER

CAST OF CHARACTERS

BEATRICE, mother
HENRY, father
MARY, aunt
JULIA, female, friend
RICKI, female, friend
EMMA, female, English teacher
ANDREW, male, friend
RACHEL, female, a ghost

SCENE 1

(Rows of chairs are set on half of the stage. They face stage left, where a coffin lies closed. BEATRICE, HENRY, MARY, JULIA, RICKI, EMMA, and ANDREW sit quietly. After a moment, Beatrice stands and walks to the coffin.)

BEATRICE: *(Addressing the crowd:)* Thank you all for coming, it means a great deal to Henry and me.

(Lights down on stage left, up on stage right where a couch, chair, mirror, toilet, and door are set. RACHEL sits on the couch, headphones plugged into her iPod, flipping through a magazine and singing along to her music.)

RACHEL: YOU THINK NOW THAT YOU'VE LOST
ALL THE FEELING IN YOUR TOES
AS THE NUMBNESS TRAVELS ROUND, YOU HAVE NO PLACE TO GO.
PERHAPS YOU WILL SUBDUE TO THE SHARP AND PIERCING AIR
STRIP OFF ALL YOUR CLOTHES AND JUST LAY THERE.
LAY THERE...
(Removing her headphones:) Mom! When's dinner?

(Pause. No response. Rachel returns to reading her magazine. Her phone rings as if she's received a text message. She picks it up and looks. She then dials a number and puts the phone to her ear.)

Ricki? Hey, it's Rache. *(Pause.)* No, no, just cause I'm reading People and I figured phone was easier. *(Pause.)* Me too! I'm starving! *(Pause.)* Yeah I took the math final today, it wasn't that bad. *(Pause.)* Yeah I'm fine, why? *(Pause.)* No, no, no everything's cool. I talked to him about it earlier. *(Pause.)* Haha I know, I know... *(Pause.)* I know! Okay enough. *(Laughing:)* It's not a big deal, I'll see you tomorrow. Okay, bye.

(Rachel hangs up the phone and stands next to her couch facing stage right, watching herself in the mirror.)

Hm.

(She pulls up her shirt to her ribcage, examining her stomach. She grabs a handful of flesh and jiggles it.)

Mirror mirror on the wall, why can't I be thin and tall?

(She spins around to look at her rear, furrowing her brow almost comically. Lights down on stage right, up on stage left.)

BEATRICE: *(Wringing her hands:)* It's been tough the last few weeks, for all of us. *(Uneasily:)* Since we're such an…intimate group, I thought it would be nice to invite you all up to say a few words and goodbyes.

(Pause. Everyone looks around at each other. Finally, Ricki stands and walks to the coffin as Beatrice sits.)

RICKI: I didn't really prepare anything, uhm… Well; Rachel was a good friend to me. She always asked about my problems with boys or my family or whatever. She was always so happy. There was this one time we were sitting in her room, and she just stood up and started dancing for no reason. That's the sort of thing I remember most, I guess, about Rachel. That look in her eyes when she'd get an idea like no matter how much you tried to convince her it wouldn't work there was no budging, that was it. She had to do it or the world would end. I admired that determination in her, and I always wished I could have had some of it myself. *(No longer addressing the crowd, but herself:)* I thought Rachel was perfect. That's not even an exaggeration; she was beautiful and so smart and funny and exciting. But she was also aloof. You could hear it in the way she'd say, "Yeah, I'm fine" and force a grin so wholeheartedly that you just let it go and moved on. She played it off well too, really making us all believe that the distance was her own choosing and maintaining an air of mystery that only made her more alluring. But she didn't want it.

(Lights down stage left. Ricki and Julia cross to center stage during blackout and are met by Rachel.)

JULIA: Hey!

(The girls hug.)

RICKI: Hey. So?! *(Leaning in. Whispering:)* Tell me what happened.

JULIA: Okay so Saturday night I went out with Caroline —

RICKI: Right.

JULIA: And she had heard that Drew was having a party —

RICKI: Mhm.

JULIA: *(Robust, excited gestures.)* Anyway we go and I'm, like, the only person from our school. It was pretty awkward at first but then I saw Jordan and was like thank god he's here, one person I know! So we're talking for a while and then this godly guy walks in, like 6 feet tall, built well I guess, not carved out of stone or anything, and he walks right over to Jordan and they start talking. So then I'm like "oh hi I'm Julia" and he says his name is Sean and we start talking cause neither of us knows that many people and Jordan's still there so it's not awkward. Then, 20 minutes later or something, the cops show up cause Drew forgot to warn the neighbors so we all run out the garage door to the park near his house. So we're all there and these two guys try to climb to the roof of the little building with the bathroom in it. I'm just sitting with Caroline and Jordan on this ledge. Then I see Sean like on a structure with this girl, I dunno who she is but I was like noooo! But so then I convince Caroline to walk over there with me and ask if they know how long we'll be in the park and so Sean comes back to the group—

RACHEL: Guys, we've gotta go to class.

JULIA: Hold on! I'm almost done!

RICKI: I hate you! Why can't I meet impossibly gorgeous men at parties on weekends and run through parks with them?

RACHEL: Okay well I'm going to class, see you guys later.

RICKI: Lunch?

RACHEL: I have student council.

RICKI: Oh, right, okay well I'll catch you later, love you.

RACHEL: Yeah.

RICKI: *(Turning back to Julia:)* Hurry! I wanna hear the end.

JULIA: Okay so he walks back over and basically what ends up happening is we walk to McDonald's in a big group and the two of us are flirting and then he and Jordan come back to Caroline's house to hang out and we all watch Hostel. By the way never watch that with guys, all they do is stare at all the naked women.

RICKI: What a surprise.

JULIA: But he was snuggling with me during the movie and it was so cute! Caroline's mom kicked everyone out at 12 but he texted me last night and said he wanted to hang out this weekend!

RICKI: Ah!!

JULIA: I know! I'm so excited.

RICKI: *(Over her shoulder as she exits:)* Okay I'm gonna run to class but that's great.

JULIA: Bye girl.

(She blows a kiss. Julia and Ricki return to the funeral as Rachel walks to stage right. She begins to do crunches, pushups and other exercises.)

RACHEL: Come on, Rache, you got this. Ten more, that's all, keep going. I can feel the fat burning off, keep pushing, work through the pain. Seven, six, five, four, three, two, one, done! *(Panting:)* Phew that felt nice.

(She stands and examines herself once more in the mirror. Lights down on stage left, up on stage right.)

RICKI: Rachel was brilliant in her sickness. She'd tell me "Ricki, I know I have a problem, and I'll work on it, okay? Just give me time. I'll be fine. It's all gonna work out, it's not like I'm throwing up or starving myself or anything." She'd say "Ricki, I had the hardest workout at the gym yesterday" and, where I used to smile and feel jealous of her dedication, I'd cringe, shrinking behind her vapid promises and pretending it wasn't my responsibility to make sure she was okay. I don't know if it's all my fault, it feels like it but really she didn't want help.

(Lights up on stage left, where Rachel is scribbling in a notebook, speaking what she is writing.)

RACHEL: *(Speaking almost frantically:)* Three sets of 10 pushups, 25 crunches, 8 jumping jacks, one minute of plank, and four glasses of water before breakfast and dinner. *(Pause.)* Tell mom to only buy organic foods and stock up on celery, it has negative calories. Oh, and no more eggs, butter, wheat, sugar, or salad dressing.

(She rips the page from her notebook and hangs it on the mirror.)

There, perfect.

(Looking at her reflection, Rachel freezes and Ricki walks to her couch and screams heartily. She calmly picks up the notebook. She reads from it.)

RICKI: It was wrong of me to read her journal. But I did it and I'm glad because now, as I look at this wooden box about to sit solitary in the soil, I know what's really being buried. I won't tell, won't breathe a word of it. But I'll keep breathing. *(Addressing the crowd at the funeral:)* Rachel was confident, courageous, and beautiful. *(Turning to the coffin:)* Bye Rache.

BEATRICE: Thank you, Ricki. That was lovely.

HENRY: I hope —

BEATICE: *(Privately, angry.)* Sh! Not now.

HENRY: But —

BEATRICE: I said not now.

(Henry sits. Pause.)

(In a forced, polite but deeply irritated tone:) Mary, would you speak?

(She motions for her.)

MARY: *(Walking to the front, tripping:)* Beats, I don't know if —

BEATRICE: *(Ushering her to the front:)* Everyone, this is my sister Mary.

MARY: *(Deep breath.)* Good afternoon.

(She mimes her speech as the scene continues with a conversation between Andrew and Julia outside the funeral. Andrew rubs the top of Julia's head. She laughs.)

JULIA: You've gotta stop doing that.

ANDREW: What?

(Julia lets out a playfully disgruntled sigh.)

Huh?

JULIA: You really need a haircut.

(She touches his hair, fixing it.)

ANDREW: You think so? *(Looking down her shirt as she works on his hair:)* I think I'm looking just fine these days.

JULIA: Oh? I don't know about that.

ANDREW: Well you should!

(Taking her wrists and moving her hands away from his head. He keeps his grip, moving her from side to side playfully.)

JULIA: *(Slaps his shoulder, giggling:)* Stop!

ANDREW: Nope. Not gonna happen.

(He begins twirling her. When he finishes, she stumbles about and giggles.)

JULIA: Hey so are you excited for the circus center?

ANDREW: No way, I'm terrified of heights.

JULIA: Oh don't worry, big bad me will be there to protect you.

ANDREW: Mhm we'll see!

JULIA: Oh yes we will. You'll be bawling like a baby —

ANDREW: Bawling like a grown-ass-man you mean!

JULIA: I dunno…

(Andrew pretends to collapse in a fit of tears. Julia laughs.)

See? This is why you need me! I can bring tissues and all the motivational banter you'll need.

ANDREW: *(Still pretending to cry:)* Oh Julia, how will I ever repay you?

(Lights down.)

SCENE 2

(Rachel rips the hair ties out of her hair and shakes it out. Andrew rises and goes to sit on the couch. Lights go down on stage right and fully up on Rachel's room scene.)

RACHEL: *(Standing in front of the mirror, picking at zits and muttering:)* Stupid acne. Great, now I'm all red.

ANDREW: Rache, will you stop and get over here? *(Kissing her:)* Mmm, yeah I think that's just what you needed. How 'bout a little more of this *(He kisses her.)* and maybe this.

(He whispers in her ear before kissing her neck.)

RACHEL: *(Giggling:)* Stop it!

ANDREW: *(Playfully:)* Oh now do you really mean that? I don't think so.

RACHEL: You know me too well.

ANDREW: Oh?? We'll see about that.

(They start making out on the couch.)

RACHEL: *(After a while:)* Baby, my mom's home.

ANDREW: *(Kissing her ears:)* Shhhh.

RACHEL: I really have to write that English paper for Mr. Meyers, and you know how he —

ANDREW: I know, I know. But once I walk out that door, you'll sit in front of your computer staring at your paper and wish you hadn't sent me away.

RACHEL: I gotta admit, you're persuasive. But I have to pass on this one.

ANDREW: Really? Aw, that's no fun.

RACHEL: Well unfortunately for us both, I can't always be the fun one.

ANDREW: *(Lightheartedly:)* Well…you are always the fun one.

RACHEL: *(Playfully:)* I try.

ANDREW: Oh, I know.

RACHEL: You really, really—?

ANDREW: Yes.

RACHEL: *(Sarcastically:)* Well, no one can stop Mr. Andrew Baker when he's on a mission. If he wants something, he gets it.

ANDREW: Mmmm, that's right. Now you stop being such a party pooper and get back over here.

RACHEL: *(Shaking her head coyly:)* Make me.

ANDREW: *(Whining:)* Rache…

RACHEL: No, no, no, you get to have your fun so let me have mine! I need to keep you interested, don't I? That's what all the magazines say, keep the hunt alive. Play hard to get!

ANDREW: Baby it doesn't have to be this difficult all the time.

RACHEL: I'm not being difficult, I'm being fun. I'm the fun one, remember?

ANDREW: Yeah, I remember. Now live up to that title and get your butt over here!

RACHEL: *(Lying down with him:)* Talking about my butt, I see. What? You think it's nice?

ANDREW: You know I do baby…it's perfect.

RACHEL: Yeah? Good.

(As they kiss, lights fade to black on stage left and come up on Beatrice standing at the back of the room arguing with her husband as the rest of the room walks slowly by the casket, some dropping flowers.)

BEATRICE: Henry, this is my daughter's funeral —

HENRY: Our daughter.

BEATRICE: And I cannot have you talking about —

HENRY: About what? The truth? Beatrice, please

BEATRICE: Don't you speak to me in that tone —

HENRY: I don't have a tone

(Beatrice lets out a huffy, hurried breath.)

Don't get huffy.

BEATRICE: I'm not huffy!

HENRY: Oh come on, look at yourself. Pay our daughter a little more respect.

BEATRICE: I am paying her all the respect I possibly can be stopping you from bringing ridiculous allegations into —

HENRY: Ridiculous alleg…? Beatrice, you and I both know Rachel had problems. Don't pretend they didn't exist just because she is gone.

BEATRICE: Problems. What does that even mean? We all have problems!

HENRY: This is ridiculous.

(He walks away. Beatrice, hands on hips, waits for everyone to take their seats. She lets out a deep sigh and goes to the front.)

BEATRICE: Would anyone else like to speak?

(Beatrice looks out over the crowd, waiting for someone to come forward. After a moment, Emma rises and walks to the front of the funeral scene. Emma takes a deep breath and all lights go out. The sound of a heart beating quickly echoes through the theater. Lights go up on Rachel kneeling at the toilet, back to the funeral scene, as Emma walks towards the toilet as if it is a school bathroom she is about to enter. Rachel is throwing up. Emma hears and begins to leave, pausing before exiting and turning back.)

SCENE 3

EMMA: Is everything alright in there?

(Silence. Rachel reaches into her throat and continues to kneel.)

Do you need help?

(Silence. As Rachel begins speaking, Emma freezes in place.)

RACHEL: If I wait long enough, they always leave. People think they want stay and help, but when it comes down to it, we can only withstand someone else's sickness for so long. So I wait and they leave, and it's as if no one even heard in the first place.

EMMA: Hello?

(Rachel begins coughing. Emma, alarmed, opens the stall door to see Rachel reaching down her throat.)

EMMA: What's going on?

RACHEL: Hi Ms. H. I am feeling really sick. I think I'll go home.

EMMA: Rachel, oh, um…you sure you're doing okay?

RACHEL: I just need to go rest.

EMMA: Okay, well why don't you go to the nurse's office and I'll call your parents.

RACHEL: Oh don't worry, I already called my mom. She's on her way.

EMMA: Oh. Alright then. Well, um, feel better.

RACHEL: Thanks Ms. H.

(Rachel leaves and sits on the unlit couch.)

EMMA: If I admit what I think I just saw, I'll have to do something. But it was probably nothing, no reason to make a big deal. She said she was sick, that's all. Calm down, Emma, Jesus, people get sick all the time. Rachel isn't one of those girls. She's intelligent, she's driven, she's creative and confident. Stop worrying so much about the kids, they can handle themselves.

(She looks back at the toilet.)

It'll be fine.

(Emma sits on the toilet.)

That's what I told myself. For months I thought "everyone has their own lives and problems and I have no idea what's actually going on, so I shouldn't butt in"...until Rachel stopped coming to school.

(Julia stands and walks towards Emma as if through a school hallway.)

Morning Julia.

JULIA: Morning Ms. H.

EMMA: How is everything?

JULIA: Pretty good, finals are coming up but besides that I'm doing well.

EMMA: Good I'm glad. And your applications?

JULIA: Just submitted my early decision last night, actually!

MARY: That's great! Where to?

JULIA: Dartmouth.

MARY: Wow well, best of luck.

JULIA: Thanks. It's just a shot in the dark, you know? Even if you're qualified it's near impossible to get into that kind of school and I don't have misconceptions —

MARY: I'm sure wherever you go you'll have a great experience.

JULIA: Yeah no totally. Same with everyone! I'm just ready to get out, meet some new people —

MARY: I remember what that was like.

JULIA: Where'd you go?

MARY: University of Miami.

JULIA: Cool.

MARY: Where are your friends looking?

JULIA: Oh you know…everyone is so freaked out by the competition they won't even tell. I don't even know!

MARY: *(Tentatively:)* How's Rachel by the way? I haven't seen her recently.

JULIA: *(Almost to herself:)* Oh. So they decided not to tell you. *(Pause.)* Well, it's not really any of my business —

EMMA: Well I knew she'd been having some…trouble.

JULIA: She told you?

EMMA: No, not exactly…

JULIA: So you saw.

EMMA: I guess you could say that, yes.

(Julia gets emotional.)

Is she okay?

JULIA: She's in the hospital. Has been for a couple days. Look, I really need to go.

(Julia rushes away from Emma towards Rachel. Rachel is lying on a hospital bed. Beatrice, Julia, Ricki, and Andrew walk to the bed and stand around it, watching Rachel.)

BEATRICE: Hey honey, you're up.

RACHEL: Hey mom.

ANDREW: Hey Rache.

RACHEL: I must look terrible.

ANDREW: You look fine, don't worry. I'm just glad you're okay.

RACHEL: Yeah.

BEATRICE: Honey, the doctor says you can leave today if you want. How're you feeling?

RACHEL: Better, a lot better.

BEATRICE: I packed all your stuff up and it's in the back of the other car. We can go whenever you want.

RACHEL: Okay. I think I'm gonna sleep a little before we go.

BEATRICE: Okay baby. Get some rest.

(Rachel closes her eyes.)

RICKI: Are you going to drop her off at the center right away?

BEATRICE: I think that's best.

RICKI: Yeah, it just feels so sudden I guess.

JULIA: Can we go visit at all?

BEATRICE: Family only for the first couple weeks is what they said is best for her health.

RICKI: That makes sense I guess. How long will she live there?

BEATRICE: For at least a month, maybe more. Until her therapist thinks she can handle being at home again.

JULIA: What about school?

BEATRICE: It'll just have to go on hold for a while. Her health is what's most important right now.

(Lights dim and Beatrice walks to the center of the stage with Mary. The women stand apart from one another, speaking on cell phones:)

Hi.

MARY: Hey.

BEATRICE: How've you been?

MARY: Fine. And you?

BEATRICE: I'm okay.

MARY: Good.

BEATRICE: Yeah.

MARY: And how's Henry?

BEATRICE: Oh he's just fine.

MARY: Good. *(Pause.)* Well everything here has been good. Robert is starting piano lessons and Kenny had his first day of kindergarten.

BEATRICE: *(With forced enthusiasm:)* Exciting!

MARY: Beatrice, why'd you call?

BEATRICE: *(Long pause. Sniffling:)* She's not eating again, Mare.

MARY: I'm sure it'll be fine —

BEATRICE: *(Hysterically, as if she is talking to herself more than* *to another person:)* It's not fine! Every night she only eats just as much as the doctor says she has to, not a crumb more. She catalogues her calories religiously in that little book of hers. I've tried hiding it from her but she throws these horrible tantrums.

(Mary strokes the back of her neck.)

Every week we go in to the office to get her weighed and looked at and nothing's getting better. He says if her weight is down again next week we have to send her back. I can't stand this house without her; Henry and I don't know what to do with ourselves anymore. I guess it might be nice to get a chance to work on my marriage for once but honestly all I ever think about is Rachel. I don't know what else to do, I covered all the mirrors with paper and put the scales in storage. I even hid the measuring tapes. I just don't know, Mary, I feel like I'm failing—

MARY: You're not failing. Your marriage is fine; you're just under a lot of stress. Remember that your daughter loves you and she'll be fine. A lot of kids develop these kinds of problems and many come out on the other side. I think the statistics are pretty low for that and besides, Rachel is strong, she'll be fine.

BEATRICE: Yeah, you're right. You should have seen all the kids at the center, pushed around in wheelchairs cause their legs were too weak to support their bodies; ribs exposed and visible even under baggy shirts. She's definitely not alone.

MARY: Right, and neither are you.

BEATRICE: Thanks.

MARY: Yeah…well call whenever you need and let me know if I can ever do anything.

BEATRICE: Okay.

MARY: Talk to you soon.

BEATRICE: Bye.

(They all return to the funeral. Emma begins talking as if picking up in the middle of a speech.)

EMMA: Rachel's respect for other people and, in my experience, reverence for adults and ability to hold really intellectually stimulating conversation was inspiring. It was great to have her in class as well as see her around campus because she fostered the kind of love of learning I want to see in every student. We will miss her so much.

(Everyone freezes besides Andrew, who turns in his chair to address the audience.)

ANDREW: There are seven people at this funeral. Only seven. *(Pause.)* I hope I have more than seven people at my funeral, Jesus. Good thing she'll never know, it'd kill her. *(Andrew rises and walks to the casket, addressing the guests:)* I've never been the type to talk in front of people, so I'll try to keep it brief. Rachel looked out on this world and saw color and life and vibrancy. She saw a being undulating with chance and reason and possibility and pain. She knew the potential of life. That's a beautiful thing.

BEATRICE: Thank you, Andrew; you're quite the eloquent young man. I'm glad Rachel knew you.

(Andrew returns to his seat.)

So unless anyone else has something to say, Henry and I would like to say our goodbyes.

(She looks out over the crowd. Julia hangs her head.)

Okay, Henry?

(Lights dim on funeral scene where Beatrice and Henry silently pay their respects as Rachel speaks. A spot comes up on Rachel, who is standing in front of the mirror, staring and talking to herself.)

RACHEL: You see, here is the inevitable part. I can sense it's coming on like the cold water from a dirty shower head, how you can feel its sting even before it reaches the skin. Funerals make us feel uncomfortable, itchy in our skin. Funerals drive us mad, make us realize our mortality. Suddenly, a lifetime is shrunk into brief moments and everything we wish we could say comes pouring out. Wives attack mistresses, brothers quarrel over antiquated issues, friends declare latent love, and all the while we know we don't really want to be doing this. But it's not our fault, no, it's the funeral home and the casket and all the black and the petals. It's the dead body's fault that those still living now live with even more regret.

(All but Julia exit.)

JULIA: I didn't want to speak at your funeral because there is nothing to say. You were sick and we all stood by, supporting you maybe but letting it happen too. Now we act like it was your time or there's some greater plan but we all know that the truth is we let you kill yourself. *(Getting fiery:)* I'm sick of dealing with eating disorders; half the people I know have them and it makes the world seem messed up and hopeless. I'm not going to let myself fall into the same trap as you, Rache. There are people dying everywhere because they don't think they're beautiful, don't think they're good enough, don't see anything worthwhile in the mirror unless they see a sliver of themselves. And it's not just appearances, no, it's control. Pressure has been mounting since we were little girls to be thinner, taller, tanner, smarter. You have to have a 4.0 and a slew of outside activities to get into any good college and on top of that you have to look like a model to have a social life at all. *(Riled up. Nearly screaming:)* I hate this society that messes with our brains and skews our priorities! I hate McDonald's, Urban Outfitters, politics and global warming. I hate diets and donuts and capitalism, I hate scales and coal and modern-day slavery! I hate California! Hollywood! I hate the models and runways and size double zeros! What the hell is that anyway? Double zero? Really?

(Deep breaths. Calming down. Shaking her head. Julia exits and after a moment Beatrice enters.)

BEATRICE: Hey Rache, it's just me now. I almost chose that blue dress I love, you always looked so good in it. But I knew you would have been unhappy so now you're wearing your flowery dress, even though it's not my favorite. *(Pause.)* I know I wasn't always a perfect mother, far less than that most of the time actually. But I did the best I could. Things are okay around the house; your father has been quiet recently. There are so many things I said to you that I wish I could take back. I'm sorry I didn't make you feel beautiful. I'm sorry I didn't give you a reason to live.

(Henry enters, motioning for his wife to leave. They walk from the funeral into Rachel's room where the People magazine lies on the couch. Beatrice sees it, picks it up and examines it. She begins to rip the pages out frantically, wailing and falling to the floor.)

(Blackout. End of play.)

The Author Speaks

What inspired you to write this play?
It is troubling that the epidemic of teen eating disorders remains pulsing just below public consciousness. I have struggled throughout my high school career with the fact that many of the young women (and even some of the young men) I see every day battle eating disorders without proper support from family, friends, or proper diagnoses from doctors. Anorexia and bulimia are not the only types to fear; binge eating and addiction to exercise are prominent and life threatening. Unfortunately, the subject is taboo. I want to see this changed.

Was the structure of the play influenced by any other work?
The play's structure was loosely influenced by Thornton Wilder's *Our Town*. The examination of past, present, and future served my desire to mesh cause with effect and action with consequence.

Have you dealt with the same theme in other works that you have written?
Not to date but I plan to again tackle the topic in a shorter one-act for my high school's one-act festival in the spring of 2012. I have written a piece about the teenage struggle with coming of age and concealing truths, but not in the context of eating disorders.

What writers have had the most profound effect on your style?
My writing transformed most profoundly after I was introduced to the works of Ariel Dorfman, Jorge Luis Borges, and Kurt Vonnegut.

What do you hope to achieve with this work?
I have dealt with a few situations in which I felt it was necessary to extend the conversation about eating disorders with a friend to involving adults, and I hope this play will stimulate others to examine their surroundings and begin these difficult but necessary conversations as well.

What inspired you to become a playwright?
I have always been deeply inspired by language. I began singing and was entranced by the poetry I was performing as lyrics. I began writing poetry to express difficult thoughts and emotions to my parents as a child and evolved into a young woman who recognizes the incredible ability of writing to portray, convince, reveal and cause change. Plays are particularly important to me because they allow for the nuances of body language and incorporate the creative abilities and inclinations of many, not simply the author.

How did you research the subject?
I researched the subject simply by living as a teenage female in San Francisco. I researched by observing my peers and examining my emotions around the situations I have encountered. I researched by involving myself in the support of friends and family when eating disorders were ravaging someone's (and thus many people's) life (lives).

Are any characters modeled after real life or historical figures?
Not directly. I combined many character traits I see in the people I know who have struggled with an eating disorder to create my main character and built a world around her that could best elucidate the complicated emotions that arise when a child dies.

Shakespeare gave advice to the players in *Hamlet*; if you could give advice to your cast what would it be?
This play is not fiction. The exact scenario and characters may be fictitious, but the battles and emotions are not. Let yourself grapple with the prevalence of this illness and commit yourself to the extension of the message: eating disorders must be understood, taken seriously, and discussed.

About the Author

Hannah Estelle Sears grew up in San Francisco and has been writing creatively since she was seven years old. She began writing one-acts in eighth grade and was a finalist in PlayGround's New Voices One-Act Writing Contest as a sophomore in high school. She has been active in theatre her whole life, performing predominantly in musicals such as *Aida*, *Footloose*, *The Music Man* and *Oklahoma*, as well as participating in a student-written and performed peer education theatre project and student-written one acts at her high school, The Urban School. She is a writer and director in The Urban School's 2012 spring one-acts festival and plans to attend Yale University in the fall. She is extremely excited to be part of YouthPLAYS and thanks her mother, father, sisters and mentors.

More from YouthPLAYS

Carolina Dive by Neeley Gossett
Drama. 30-35 minutes. 2 1 males, 5-10 females. (7-12 performers possible, plus extras).

Jenna is a teenager living in a place known only for race cars and beauty pageants. When her friends discover an old bridge, diving off it becomes her obsession. Her strange, solitary nighttime practices make her an outcast, but the possibility of diving for a college team gives her a way to escape the small town. When a dive damages her inner ear and she can no longer keep her balance, however, her future plans are put in jeopardy.

The Totally Life Changing Letter That Doesn't Really Matter by Marisa Kanai
Comedy. 15-20 minutes. 2-9 males, 3-9 females (7-15 performers possible).

A high school senior, Lily, has applied to college. The letter that will seal her fate is now in her hands. Should she open it? As she contemplates this potentially life changing event, the play takes a comic look back at the application process and her journey through the wacky, pressure-filled world of high school academics that's led her to where she is now.

You're Next by Jonathan Dorf
Drama. 15-20 minutes. 2 males.

Jay's been throw into the shower—again. As he huddles with his best friend Peter in search of a solution to his bullying problem, Peter reveals that he's brought a gun for Jay to use against his tormentor. But when Jay hesitates and Peter won't let up, it gradually becomes clear that Jay's not the only one who needs help...

Un-Holy Nite by Samantha Macher
Comedy with music. 40-50 minutes. 7-13 males, 2-9 females (9-21 performers possible).

Five comic Christmas vignettes are themed around the (public domain) Christmas carol that accompanies them--perfect for the school that wants to do a showcase of both actors and singers for a holiday performance. The stories range from guys hanging out at a holiday sweater party waiting for girls to show up (*Jingle Belles*) to a story about a mysterious Christmas present waiting to be opened (*It Came Upon a Midnite Clear*). There's something in this series of holiday comedies for everyone.

The Stalking Horse by Ed Shockley
Drama. 90-110 minutes. 5-20 males, 5-20 females (includes speaking roles, as well as roles for drummers and dancers; 10-40 performers possible).

Mkuu, the great hunter and village leader, is dying. Upepo, the heir apparent, uses intimidation and deception to insure that he assumes the throne and wins the village beauty. He succeeds at exiling his only rival, Maji, a hapless sheepherder who has been magically instructed in the art of hunting. Famine befalls the village as a mysterious beast begins preying upon the hunters whenever they dare venture into the bush. Finally Maji battles the monster alone and returns to compete for command of the village with a surprising result that proves the adage, "Be careful what you wish for."

Did you know that **www.youthplays.com** has dozens of monologues that are free for use in the classroom and for auditions? Go there today!

Printed in Great Britain
by Amazon

79588073R00020